MY MAGICAL TREE

My Magical Tree has been designed to help children navigate through the stresses and strains of daily life and bring them back into balance. It can help them when they are ungrounded and finding it hard to concentrate and focus both at home and at school.

There are many reasons why a child may be having problems with their focus, attention and concentration. It could be lack of sleep, poor nutrition; they may not be feeling well, a growth spurt, environmental factors etc. Encouraging a child to calm, centre and balance themselves can lead to improved focus and concentration, which will promote success at school and will have a positive effect on their confidence and self-esteem.

As you go through the book you will notice that your child will start to become more settled, calm and relaxed, We recommend that before you begin, you create a calm environment and allow your child to take a moment before reading the book. You might like to put on some relaxing music and when you see that they are a little more settled, then you can begin.

Go through the book with your child and make the choices together so that you can discuss the translations of each choice at the end. The translations will give you an idea of what your child is experiencing and will create a natural conversation, as well as giving you ideas on how to help them. The child may even feel safe enough to open up to you and so it will help if you allow the conversation to mostly come from them and just see where it goes. Ask them if they feel the translation is accurate to how they are feeling. You may learn far more than you expected.

The choices represent what the child is experiencing in this moment. Each time they go through it, they will most likely choose completely different things and this is because emotionally they will be in a different place. If you have a child who always chooses the same thing then you could maybe work with a second choice and see if that is a better reflection of what is going on.

Use the book as often as you like. When used regularly it can really help the child to grasp the technique and they can use it in their day to day lives, even when the book is not to hand. It can become a life long skill.

TERRY ALLEN ★ JACQUI GRAY

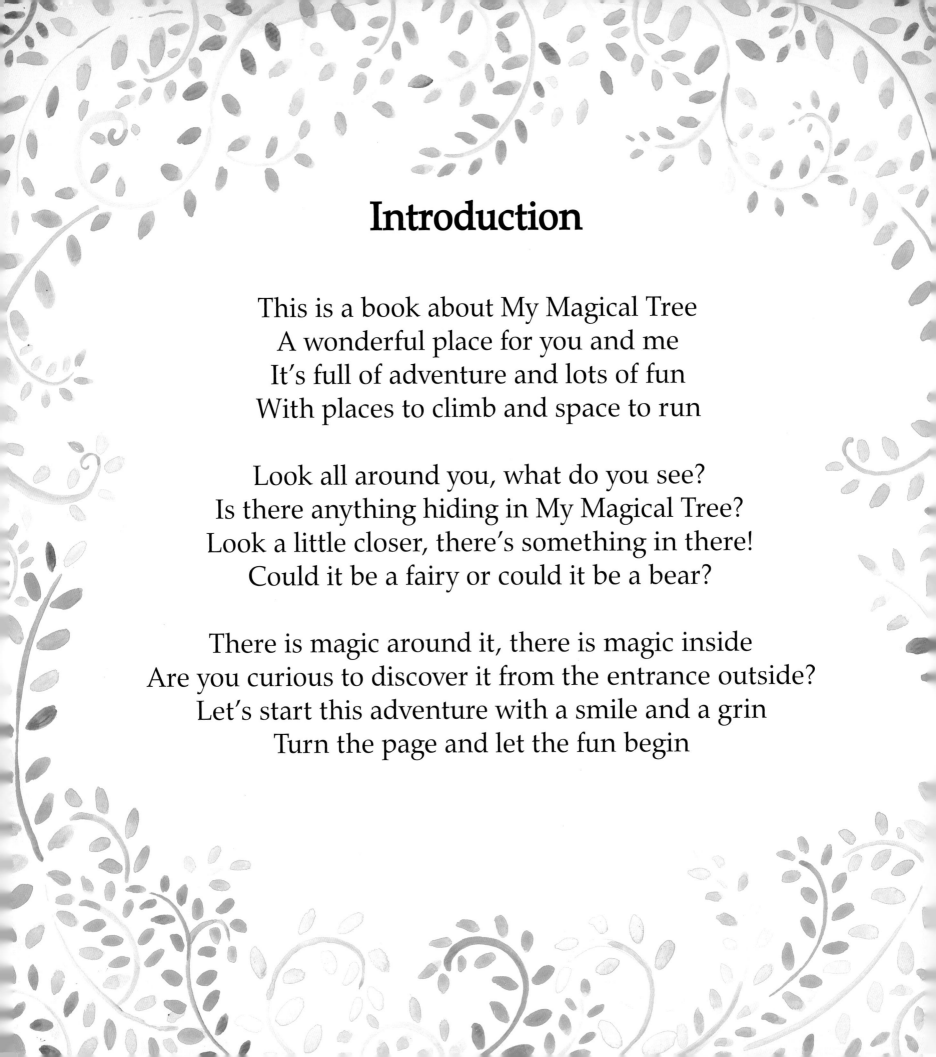

Introduction

This is a book about My Magical Tree
A wonderful place for you and me
It's full of adventure and lots of fun
With places to climb and space to run

Look all around you, what do you see?
Is there anything hiding in My Magical Tree?
Look a little closer, there's something in there!
Could it be a fairy or could it be a bear?

There is magic around it, there is magic inside
Are you curious to discover it from the entrance outside?
Let's start this adventure with a smile and a grin
Turn the page and let the fun begin

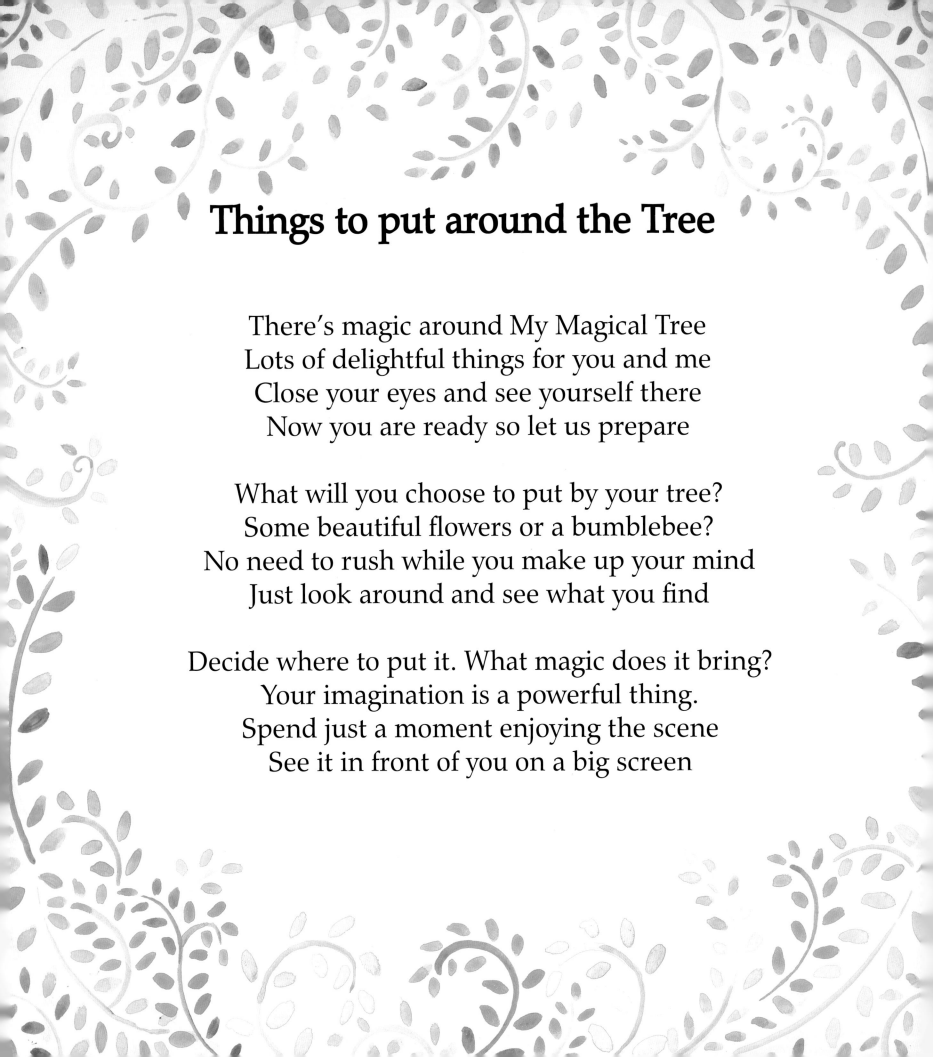

Things to put around the Tree

There's magic around My Magical Tree
Lots of delightful things for you and me
Close your eyes and see yourself there
Now you are ready so let us prepare

What will you choose to put by your tree?
Some beautiful flowers or a bumblebee?
No need to rush while you make up your mind
Just look around and see what you find

Decide where to put it. What magic does it bring?
Your imagination is a powerful thing.
Spend just a moment enjoying the scene
See it in front of you on a big screen

Bee

Flowers

Birds

Snake

Butterfly

Owl

Snail

Wolf

Ladybird

Bear

Porcupine

Frog

Magical Doors

This magical tree has a door to explore
It's very exciting so let us learn more
Choose very carefully and be very wise
This is the entrance to a wonderful surprise

The doors are all different, so which one will it be?
The one with 'Keep Out' or the one that feels free?
It's tricky to choose, but one will feel right
Which one of these doors would you like to invite?

Now see the door at the bottom of your tree
Open it up and - what do you see?
Step inside for some adventure and fun
Are you curious? Now the magic's begun

Magical Door

Rainbow Door

Fun Door

Keep Out Door

Mystery Door

No Entry Door

Welcome Door

Do Not Disturb Door

Love Door

How to get down

Now you're inside the magical tree
It's time to go down, deep down and see
Remember it's magical so there's nothing to fear
Just go with the flow and all will be clear

How will you choose to go deep underground?
The fireman's pole or will you climb down?
Decide if you want to go fast or go slow
Once you are ready then get set and go!

As you go down to the roots of the tree
How are you feeling and what can you see?
Deeper and deeper you feel yourself travel
The next part of the adventure is about to unravel

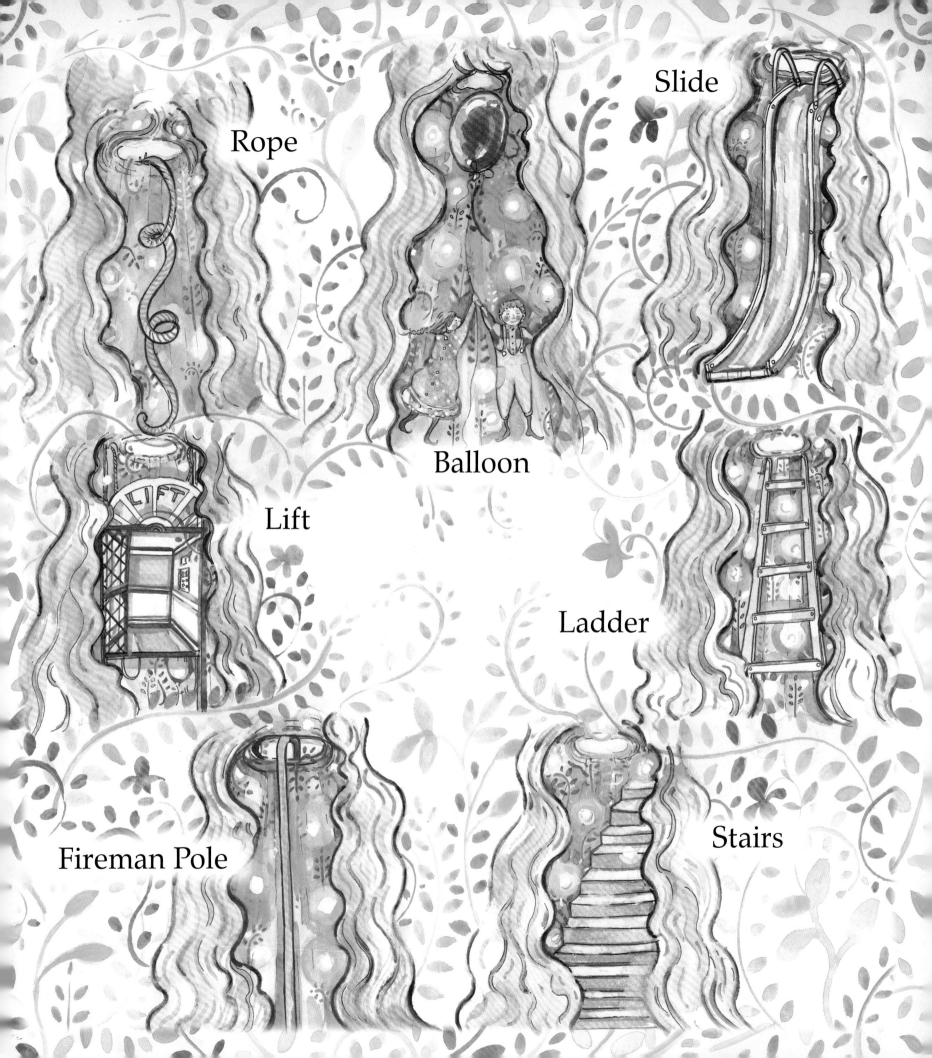

Rope

Balloon

Slide

Lift

Ladder

Fireman Pole

Stairs

Magical Rooms

Now you are down inside the magical tree
There is more to discover and much more to see
Seven great rooms, which one stands out?
You will pick the perfect one, there is no doubt

Decide how you're feeling, what mood are you in?
Maybe it's time to go deep down within
Is it time to be creative with music or magic?
Whichever you choose it will be totally fantastic!

There is something for everyone right here on this page
You could lie in the hammock or sit in the cave
Each room is unique, each room holds a gift
Whichever you choose is designed to uplift

Cosy Room

Play Room

Cave

Kitchen

Art and Music Room

Magical Room

Science Room

Magical Items

There is great excitement with the gifts on this page
Each item is magic and helps in different ways
Look at them all and then close your eyes
One of them will show you a lovely surprise

Which one do you need for this special day?
Think of what's happening around you today
What do you need help with, what's going on?
Which item can help all the problems be gone?

You could disappear right now with the magical ring
Or wave the wand and change into a king!
The magic surrounds you while you are here
There is only adventure, there is nothing to fear

Magic Lamp

Bag of Crystals

Magic Beans

Magical Ring

Magical Feather

Magic Box

Magical Wand

Magic Potion

Magical Cloak

Picture Frames

Every room needs a picture, to hang on the wall
A memory, a person or a tree standing tall
A lovely reminder of something important
You may need just one or perhaps an assortment?

When you have picked one then close your eyes
Where will you hang it and what is its size?
Is it enormous or is it just small?
Perhaps it is covering the entire wall?

Does it make you feel special or does it fill you with pride?
Or maybe it is somewhere that you'd like to hide
A person, a place or perhaps even a star
Whichever one you choose will be the best by far

Favourite Place

Trophy

Superwoman

Superman

Special Friend

I'm A Star

Pet or Animal

Family Portrait

Imaginary Friends

We'd all like to have an imaginary friend
To play with, to read with and even pretend
They give you the courage and they make you feel strong
To try different things as you go along.

They'll help you feel happy, they'll help you to smile
They will happily be with you mile after mile
So choose one you'd like and give them a name
Invite them to join you in a marvellous game

They want to be with you, they want to help out
This is the truth so try not to doubt
Enjoy being with them and have lots of fun
They will always remind you that you're the special one

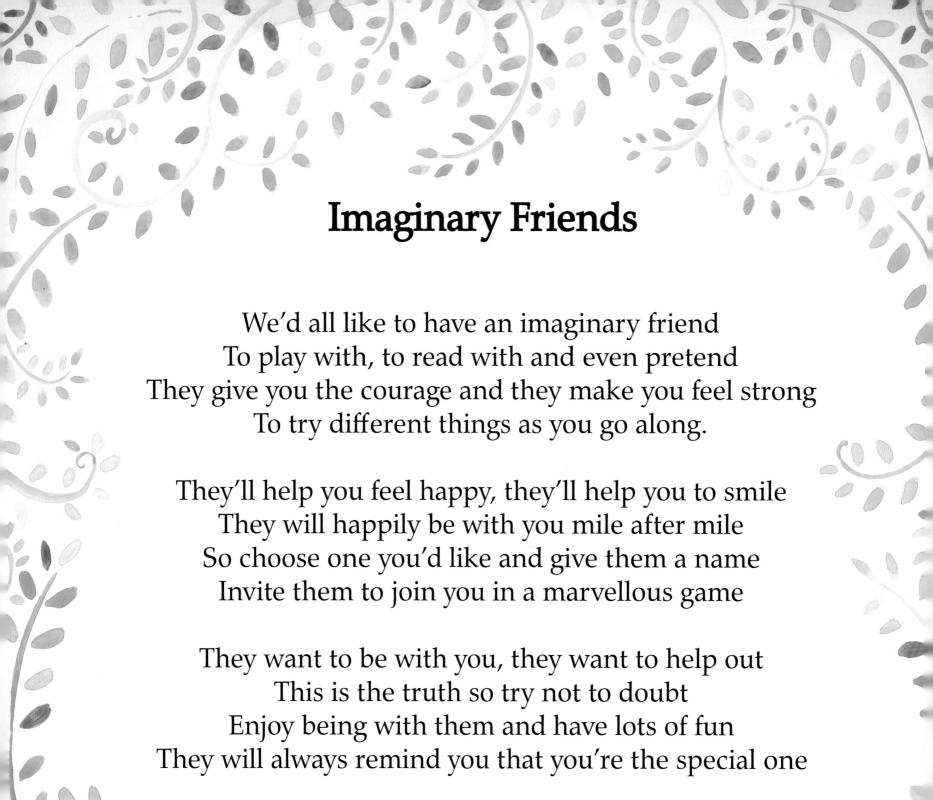

Shape
Shifter

Nature
Fairy

Nature
Fairy

Fairy
God
Mother

Giant

Pegasus

Robot

Genie

Boy &
Girl

Outside the Tree

So now we are back outside My Magical Tree
It is lovely and sunny and you feel so free
Now stand beside it and look all around
From the top of the tree right down to the ground

You might want some fun or you might want to rest
Just always remember that you are the best
What do you feel like? What will you choose?
Or maybe you just feel like having a snooze.

Swinging or climbing or reading a book
There are lots of good choices, just take a look
Have a good think until you are ready to decide
You may even feel that you just want to hide

Tree House

Climbing

Hiding

Resting

Swing

Reading

Watering
The Flowers

Campfire

A Magical End

You have now been inside My Magical Tree
So just take a moment, what magic did you see?
Think very closely about how you are feeling
Your magical tree is very appealing!

There's one piece of magic that you'll soon get to know
When you enter the tree and go down below
You will remember the truth that you are very special
And you will also remember that you are full of potential

So visit the tree whenever you desire
It is a place full of magic, a place to inspire
Create your adventures and try to have fun
We hope you enjoyed it and now you are done!

I AM SPECIAL

APPENDIX

Each item that your child chooses to go in and around their tree will have a specific meaning. Please see below the different meanings for each page in the book. Encourage your child to go through this book and make choices on a weekly basis to promote emotional wellbeing.

Things to go around the tree.

1. Snake – The snake represents grounding and a connection to mother earth. Choosing a snake means that your child is going through a time of healing and self-growth. Just as a snake sheds its skin, your child may be going through a shedding of old emotions allowing new ones to emerge. Your child may need to slow down, and enjoy the fun side of life more. Guided visualisations for grounding, yoga and mindfulness techniques may help your child to slow down and be in the present moment. As snakes rely mostly on their senses of smell and touch, your child may respond well to essential oils and massage at this time.

2. Butterfly – Your child may be going through a period of growth and transformation. They need lots of nurturing as they change and grow. They are coming into full bloom. This is a great time for your child to try visualisations, yoga, journaling, and vision boards. Encourage them to have open chats about their feelings with mum or dad. Give your child opportunities to be more independent.

3. Bird – Birds represent freedom. This is a time for your child to express and explore who they want to be. It is a good time for them to be with friends and just to be themselves. Regular meditation will enable your child to tap into their inner voice and start to trust and get to know their inner feelings. Allow them freedom to be with friends and to do hobbies. Your child may benefit from lots of visual stimulation at this time e.g. colouring mandalas, building lego etc.

4. Flowers – Flowers represent our feminine side. Your child's feminine side needs nurturing so that they can come into full bloom. Your child may need to explore and release emotions as they start to notice and become aware of their feminine side. If your child is finding it hard to focus and concentrate, spend more time outside as this will help them to recharge. Using Bach flower remedies and essential oils would be good for them.

5. Bee - Home life is very important to your child. The love of the family, working together as one, wholesome communication, balance, stability and harmony are all top priorities in your child's life. They may enjoy working as a part of a team in order to achieve things. They may also enjoy being organised and as busy as a bee! The bee's most prominent sense is smell.

Your child would benefit from essential oils especially while they are studying. This will help them to focus. Cooking and being in nature may also be good for your child at this time.

6. Ladybird - Ladybirds are connected to the spiritual and magical side of life. They signify passion, action and achievement. Choosing the ladybird means that your child is self-reliant and seeks freedom. Sometimes by being self-reliant, your child may have a tendency to suppress their feelings. This can affect the sense of balance within your child. Keeping communication channels open is very important as this helps your child release any emotions. Your child's intuition is strong, so bringing in regular visualisation, mindfulness, breathing techniques, yoga and the use of essential oils will help them to realign themselves from within.

7. Wolf – Your child is very loyal to those close to them. Trust and honesty are very important to them. The family is the centre of their life and if everything is good at home, then so are they. If their home life is unsettled this can bring in fear and uncertainty. Trust needs to be a strong feature of their home life. Your child may have a great instinct about different people and situations. They need freedom to explore, so do check that your child is getting the freedom he or she needs. Spending time in nature and using essentials oils is good for your child. The wolf is very family orientated so your child would also benefit from family activities.

8. Porcupine – Your child may be lacking joy at this present time. They may need to connect to all childlike things like imagination, fantasy, fun, creativity, music, and the joy of being with others. At present your child may feel fearful and reserved. The spikes of the porcupine represent prickly emotions and a need for your child to protect him or herself. Your child is very sensitive and can easily be upset, so others should pay attention to how they treat and speak to them. If your child has chosen this animal, then using audio (e.g. a mindfulness CD) will help them to stay focused.

9. Bear – Your child needs rest and relaxation at this time as too much may be going on in their lives. The bear is a strong animal, but unless it has time to restore and hibernate it becomes agitated and fearful. Your child is very protective of others and will stand up for him or herself. To help your child stay balanced and focused, use music, essential oils and visual activities.

10. Frog - Frogs represent a cleansing of your child's emotions, diet and lifestyle. This means that your child needs to refresh their mind, body and spirit. They can do this by eating lots of healthy food, drinking plenty of water and de-cluttering their mind and emotions. This may also be a good time to de-clutter your child's bedroom. Your child will benefit from guided visualisations, a healthier diet and a crystal salt lamp in their room.

11. Owl – Your child needs time to sit, concentrate and reflect at this time. Your child is very intuitive and wise . Your child needs quiet time so that they can tap into this intuitive creative energy. Your child loves honesty and openness and if they do not get this from their family or friends then they will search for it. They are very protective of their family. The owl's predominant sense is hearing, therefore music, audio books or guided visualisations would be of benefit to your child. Anything audio will help with their learning too.

12. Snail – Your child needs to feel protected and safe at this time. Perhaps there have been many changes going on in his or her life. Give your child time to slow down at home or school. Your child likes to take their time with things and doesn't like to be rushed. They are patient and sensitive. They don't mind being alone as they need quiet time to help them maintain balance. A snail uses its sense of touch more than anything else. Therefore your child would respond well to massage, play dough and any other hands-on activities.

Doors

1. Rainbow Door – Your child has the ability to spread love and joy to others. They are positive and happy and they enjoy helping others. They love to smile, be helpful and to make everyone around them feel uplifted. They are very expressive and enjoy learning new things. They must remember to recharge themselves by having quiet time alone and spending time in nature. Guided visualisations and magnesium salt baths are also good at this time. Make sure they are drinking enough water and have a well balanced diet.

2. Magical Door – Your child loves anything to do with crystals, nature, fairies, and unicorns. They have a great imagination, which can be enriched with guided visualisations. They must remember to ground themselves regularly. So lots of play outside in nature, massage their feet with essential oils, trampolining and any jumping or running activities.

3. Keep Out Door – Your child is feeling introverted and secretive. They need their own space to recharge. Creative activities would be very beneficial for your child at this time. Art, music and guided visualisations are a great way for them to express themselves and realign their energies. It would be helpful to create a communication box so that your child can use this to express their emotions.

4. No Entry Door - Your child may feel angry, hurt, misunderstood or frustrated. Somewhere at home there may be a lack of balance. Choosing this door may be a call for help. Give your child an opportunity to express themselves through creativity, play and fun. This is a good time to spend some one on one time with your child.

5. Welcome Door – Your child is warm and caring and likes to look after others. They are very welcoming but they can have a tendency to look after others before themselves. They are concerned about how others are feeling and empathize when someone is unhappy or sad. They always try to comfort those around them. They easily absorb the emotions of others. Your child would benefit from lots of time in nature, regular visualisations, yoga, breathing techniques, journaling and art so that they can release and restore energy.

6. Love Door – Your child is all about love. They love their family, friends, animals and nature. Your child may be very sensitive and could become insecure if they are not receiving enough love and attention. For them, everything revolves around being loved and loving other people. They need to be told they are loved every day and may even benefit from having their own pet.

7. Fun Door – Your child is outgoing and loves doing fun activities. They love positivity and happy like-minded people. They have a light energy about them and like to see the positive side of life. They need lots of interesting, different and fun things to do.

8. Do Not Disturb Door – This is a time when your child may feel the need for some quiet time and the opportunity to be by themselves. Try and respect their privacy and just allow them to choose whether they want to be alone or join in with others. Let the choice come from your child at this time.

9. Mystery Door – Your child is very trusting at this time and happy to go with the flow. They're Imagination maybe heightened and so creative activities would be good for them. They don't necessarily want a rigid routine and maybe happy with a more relaxed approach. They may enjoy the adventure of trying new things and so this could be a good opportunity to introduce them to a new activity or hobby.

Inside the Tree

1. Slide – Your child likes to move fast and quickly towards their destination at this time. Help them to slow down so that they gain more control over what is happening around them. Rushing into things can create problems so remind them to pace themselves. Breathing techniques, creativity and being outside in nature can help.

2. Rope – Your child is strong and determined. Your child may have overcome major challenges and they feel that they can now move forward. Your child is a risk taker and is not feeling fearful at this time.

3. Lift – Your child knows exactly what he or she wants and how to get there. They are practical and clever and they know where they want to go at this time in their life. Your child is in a good space.

4. Ladder – Your child is a little bit cautious at this time. They like to be in control of what they are doing and take their time to do it. They can be fearful in situations where they feel they have a lack of control. Be aware of situations that make your child feel uncomfortable and give them opportunities to talk about it. Encourage them to come up with their own solution when a problem arises, so that they can deal with it better when they come across a similar situation.

5. Fireman Pole – Your child is ambitious and determined at this time. However their choice suggests that they may jump into a situation too quickly without enough thought. This may cause them to feel insecure and out of control. Your child may be living too much in their head. Aromatherapy foot massage can help centre and balance your child. Being outside in nature and practising breathing techniques, yoga or martial arts can also be beneficial.

6. Balloon – Your child may seem be living too much in their head. They tend to daydream and often seem to float off. They are normally very creative and have wonderful ideas. They need to ground and centre themselves on a regular basis. To help with this give them lots of healthy food and regular exercise outside. Super brain yoga and essential oils in the home can also be beneficial. Give your child lots of time to be creative and find out what ignites their passion.

7. Stairs – Your child may feel insecure. Something may have happened recently that has triggered this fear and emotional sensitivity. Your child needs lots of reassurance that they are doing the best that they can. Praise them whenever possible and give them lots of opportunities to express themselves. Set up a communication box.4 Provide appropriate activities for your child to build their confidence.

Rooms

1. Cosy room – Your child needs time to relax and unwind. They need this time to help them feel centred and balanced. Encourage them to be quiet, away from computers and any other distractions. This quiet time could be spent reading a favourite book or doing guided visualisations.

2. Playroom – Your child needs time to play and have fun. Your child needs time to just be a child. This enhances your child's creativity, imagination, and problem solving skills. Could your child's life be a bit too structured at the moment?

3. Cave – Your child needs some time to retreat away from daily life. They may feel that too much is going on at the moment. They may be in need of solitude and nature. It is possible that something may have happened that has made them unhappy or simply that there is too much going on in their lives. Let your child connect to the elements around them. Allow them to just be themselves. Respect your child's need to retreat at this time and find ways to communicate with them so that you can find out the real source of their problem. Spend lots of quality time with your child and give them lots of emotional support.

4. Kitchen – Family life is very important to your child. Spend time together as a family and come together as a family for meal times. Allow your child to be creative and let them help with the cooking. Give your child chores to do as they will enjoy helping.

5. Art & Music Room – Expose your child to their creative side on a regular basis. This will help them to express themselves and bring about more balance in their lives. It can also give them time to disconnect from every day life and lift their spirits. This is a good time to introduce your child to a musical instrument. Give them access to a big arts and crafts box.

6. Science Room – Your child may find it hard to concentrate at this time. Choosing the science room means that they may benefit from doing scientific activities as it will bring them into focus. It will minimise disruptive behaviour, daydreaming and frustration. Your child needs to channel their thoughts into something concrete. Encourage your child to be curious.

7. Magical Room – Emphasize to your child how unique they are. Give your child lots of opportunities to enter into their own imaginative world, away from all technology and every day life. Give your child support to unleash their imagination. A great way they can do this is by dressing up as magical characters. Let them choose some personal crystals and encourage them to listen to guided visualisations. It's a great idea for parents to join in with their child's magical games and to encourage this type of play.

Magical Items

1. Bag of Magic Beans – Your child is going through a period of growth and change at this time. They may need support to overcome any fears they may have about themselves. Encourage them to enjoy the simple pleasures of life, like being in nature, playing with friends, spending time with their parents and using their imagination. This will help them feel present and grounded. Limit the use of iPads and media related games and encourage them to use their intuition and creativity. It's important to encourage your child to value gratitude and to help them do this every day.

2. Magic Lamp – Your child may be feeling insecure. They may not trust themselves. It could be that your child is looking for support at this time. Building your child's confidence is important, so that they can start to believe in themselves.

3. Magical Ring – Your child may be having friendship issues or issues within the family at this time. Choosing the magical ring means that your child is very trusting and loyal and needs others to have the same values. They need to feel secure through other people treating them with openness and honesty.

4. Magical Feather – Choosing the feather means that your child communicates in a graceful and knowledgeable manner. Your child is very creative. They would benefit from tapping into their creative writing skills and they may prefer working with pens, pencils and books rather than with technology.

5. Magical Box – Your child may be experiencing a lot of emotions at this time. They need to open up more within themselves and others. It could be that they are holding onto too many emotions. Creating a communication box at home would be a great way to help your child to release these emotions. They could decorate the box and place all their worries into the box. This will help them to clear out any blocked emotions. Allow your child more freedom and independence.

6. Magical Wand – Your child's thoughts may be scattered at this time and choosing the wand suggests that they need to focus on one thing at a time. To help your child to be more focused, look at their diet, exercise and water intake. Having good sleeping patterns, magnesium salt baths and foot massages may help your child at this time.

7. Magic Potion – Your child may need to be reminded of their strengths at this time. They may be lacking in confidence. Pay close attention to your child when they are with friends and in certain situations. Notice what is going on and how they are handling themselves in front of others. Provide opportunities for them to speak up and do more activities as this can help raise their self esteem.

8. Magical Cloak – Choosing the cloak means that your child may be feeling shy at this time and that they feel they can disappear and move around without anyone noticing where they are. They may wish to be invisible to others, to camouflage into the background and just observe. Your child needs some alone time to just think and recharge. If your child is normally shy, then maybe encourage them to do drama, dance, singing or to join the Brownies or Scouts.

9. Bag of Crystals - Your child has a good connection to their inner self, however they maybe lacking in energy at this time. Allow them to be in nature as much as possible as this can help them to re-energise and find balance. A good diet, quiet time and less technology can also help.

Picture Frames

1. Family portrait - Family is extremely important to your child. They may need to spend more time with the family than with friends. Ensure that you go on outings as a family as well as doing things like eating or walking together.

2. Favourite place – A favourite place is somewhere that your child chooses when they want to fully relax, be themselves and to feel free and at peace. Your child may benefit from being allowed to be in situations that allow them to be their authentic self.

3. Special Friend Boy & Girl - Your child may have a special friend and choosing this picture may mean that they would like to spend more time with them. If your child doesn't have a special friend, this may be something that they would like to have. Try and provide situations where your child can meet other children. Find an activity that your child loves doing so that they can connect to other children who enjoy the same thing.

4. Pet or Animal – Your child may be going though a period of sensitivity. They need to feel loved and accepted to feel that they are special. Allow your child to have more quiet time and reassure your child that they are loved and appreciated. This is a good time to approach your child and suggest playing a game with them or reading a story together.

5. Trophy – Your child may wish to feel special and to stand out at this time. Have lots of positive conversations with them and remind your child that although the trophy is a symbol of achievement and success, all success comes from within. Reassure your child that they are special and unique.

6. I'm A Star – This could mean that your child is going through a very confident phase or it could mean that your child wants people to notice them. Nurture your child's gifts and talents. Help your child to find their passion by allowing them to experience new things.

7. Superman & Superwoman – Your child is going through many positive changes at this time. They will benefit from your support, strength, honesty and openness; explain to your child what you expect from them. Allow your child to express how they are feeling about certain situations. By respecting your child you will encourage your child to respect you. If your child chooses a super hero or heroine, this indicates that they have all the answers to their questions but they just need a little guidance to allow them to trust their instincts. Allow your child to find their own inner power.

Imaginary Friends

1. Giant – Your child may be looking for strength, support and balance at this time. Your child may need stability and they may benefit from a routine. They would benefit by being outside more in nature and away from technology. This is an earthy giant so your child needs more connection to nature.

2. Pegasus - Your child may have heightened intuition and sensitivity at this time. They are very aware of the energy around them and would benefit from more quiet time to allow them to recharge. Spending time in nature and guided visualisations are beneficial at this time. Allow your child to have days that are unstructured with no plans so that they can just play.

3. Imaginary Friend Boy & Girl – Your child may be feeling lonely at this time. They are looking for a special connection to someone. Create opportunities for your child to mix with other children with the same interests. Depending on your child's interests, you could look at joining the Brownies, Scouts, or a swimming club.

4. Nature Fairy Boy & Girl - Fairies are connected to nature and sensitivity. Your child may like to be carefree and spontaneous. They love animals and nature. They tend to go off with the fairies, so daily grounding techniques are the key to keeping them down to earth and focused.

5. Robot – Choosing a robot may mean that your child is running on autopilot. They may be doing routine tasks without their minds being fully engaged. Your child needs to break away from rigid routines and be more creative. This can be achieved by doing art, music, dance, yoga etc.... Your child needs a break from technology.

6. Fairy Godmother – Your child may be feeling insecure about certain aspects of their life at this time. They need to know that they can overcome these insecurities by themselves, however they will benefit from help, guidance and support from those around them.

7. Shape shifter – Your child has a lot of inner strength. They also have a great imagination. Your child may need lots of freedom at this time. They would benefit from less rigidity, less control and more flow in their lives. Your child would benefit from activities that have a lot of attention to detail e.g. science projects, art etc...

8. Genie - Represents creativity, power of the mind and magic. Allow your child to tap into their creative side and bring a little magic into their lives through pretend play, fairy tales, art etc. As a genie is all about granting wishes, ask your child what it is they wish for at this moment in time.

Outside the Tree

1. Tree House – Your child may need more privacy, independence, freedom and time alone. Allow them to choose who they spend time with.

2. Climbing in the Tree – If your child has chosen to climb the tree they may be adventurous, brave and inquisitive. Your child is in a good place and so encourage these qualities.

3. Swing – Your child may be very carefree and happy within themselves at the moment, enjoying the little things in life.

4. Hiding in the Tree – Your child may be feeling fearful at this time or they may be wanting more attention. Either way, spend time with your child and give them opportunities to tell you how they are feeling. Encourage them to express themselves through creativity. Spend more quality time with your child.

5. Watering the flowers – Your child may need lots of nurturing at this time. Flowers represent gifts of love, happiness, fun and friendship, so it's important that parents nurture their child's gifts.

6. Campfire - Your child may benefit from being in groups with their friends, having fun, socialising, getting back to basics and being away from technology. Allow them plenty of time to connect with nature.

7. Reading in the Tree – Your child is happy to be in their own company. They are happy to have time alone to just be themselves.

8. Resting in the Tree – Your child may be feeling very relaxed, happy and content at this time. This choice could also mean that your child would benefit from some time out or rest.

TIPS

Himalayan Salt Lamps: Salt Lamps are wonderful and can be used in any area of the home where you would like the air quality to be improved. They create a calm and relaxing environment and provide multiple health benefits, including enhancing immunity, improving sleep and helping with the relief of migraines.

Diet – Encourage your child to eat healthily. A balanced diet has an overall effect on behaviour, concentration and general wellbeing. Choose healthy snacks and beverages that contain less sugar for your child and avoid processed foods.

Magnesium Salt Baths – Magnesium helps to sooth and relax tired aching muscles especially after exercise or sport. If your child is having difficulty sleeping, magnesium can help to promote better sleep. Many people find that they are deficient in magnesium.

Vitamin D – Vitamin D is important for growth, healthy bones and the overall vitality of your child. Due to lifestyle changes, there has been a dramatic drop in the levels of Vitamin D in some children.

Foot Massage – If your child is usually lively and energetic, a massage after their evening bath is a lovely gentle way to relax and soothe them, as well as encouraging a good night's sleep. It's also a great way to ground your child's energy and helps with focus and concentration.

Exercise – Is good for grounding Exercise helps to increase body awareness, therefore bringing the mind into the present moment.

Water – Not drinking enough water can cause fatigue, loss of concentration, headaches and even nausea in severe cases. Keeping your child hydrated can help them to perform better in school.

Guided Visualisation – The benefits of guided visualisations for children include an overall sense of calmness and increased concentration. A guided visualisation will relax your child's mind and body and bring them into the present moment.